PASSIONELLA
and other stories

Passionella

and other stories

by Jules Feiffer

COLLINS, St. James's Place, London

The story "Passionella" first appeared in Pageant,
but was completely revised and redrawn for this book.
The story "Boom" first appeared in The Village Voice.
"Passionella" and "Boom" both appeared in The Observer.

Jules Feiffer, 1957, 1959
Library of Congress Catalogue Card Number 59-10117
First Published in Great Britain 1960
Printed in Great Britain
Collins Clear-Type Press: London and Glasgow

Passionella

ELLA

was a chimneysweep.

She worked in a big office building downtown.

But it wasn't what she really wanted to do.
As she often tried to tell people:

Every night after work Ella would go home to her lonely furnished room, and there she'd sit, all night, in front of the TV and think but one thought:

IF I
COULD
ONLY
BE A
BEAUTIFUL
GLAMOROUS
MOVIE
STAR.

And that was how she spent her days -

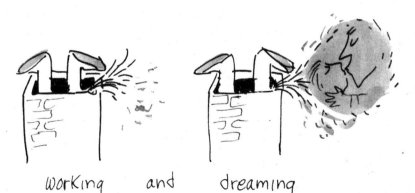

working   and   dreaming

Then one day Ella's employer came to her chimney and said: "ELLA
WE
WON'T
NEED
YOU
AFTER
NEXT
WEEK.
AUTOMATION
HAS
COME
TO
CHIMNEY
SWEEPING."

Ella was unemployed!

For weeks she wandered the streets looking for work. But nowhere was a good old-fashioned craftswoman needed.

She began to go hungry.

Television was her only escape. From the time she arrived home till the time she fell asleep, her eyes never wandered from the screen.

SOMEDAY
I WILL
BE A
BEAUTIFUL
GLAMOROUS
MOVIE
STAR.

Then one evening (it was the night of the full moon),
Ella returned from a thankless day of job hunting,
turned on the set and ...there was no picture!

She stood before the TV stunned, disbelieving, her
eyes searched the screen for the trace of an image.

NO PICTURE

NO PICTURE

NO PICTURE

Then Ella heard a voice:

HELLO OUT THERE!
THIS IS YOUR
FRIENDLY
NEIGHBORHOOD
GODMOTHER
COME TO
BRING YOU
THE ANSWER
TO YOUR
MOST
CHERISHED
DREAMS!

YOU ARE NOW ALL YOU
EVER WANTED TO BE.
HENCEFORTH YOU SHALL
BE KNOWN AS
PASSIONELLA!
THIS IS YOUR FRIENDLY
NEIGHBORHOOD
GODMOTHER RETURNING
YOU TO YOUR
LOCAL NETWORK.

Ella could not believe her eyes. She was dazzling.
"NOW I SHALL BECOME A BEAUTIFUL, GLAMOROUS MOVIE STAR!"
she said and she ran off to El Morocco—

where she met Ed Sullivan, Walter Winchell, Earl Wilson and Cholly Knickerbocker - all of whom promised to do columns on her. And this also happened:

"I AM A FAMOUS MOTION PICTURE PRODUCER, COME TO THE STUDIO TOMORROW MORNING AND I WILL SIGN YOU TO A LIFETIME CONTRACT."

Passionella went home bursting with joy. The next morning, without bothering to look in the mirror, she rushed off to the movie studio.

LIFETIME CONTRACT? ARE YOU OUT OF YOUR HEAD?

There she was — her homely old self.

Then it was all just a dream!

Ella walked the streets
till the sun set.
'IM NOT ASKING MUCH'
she brooded.
ITS NOT AS IF I WANT
TO BE A **RICH** BEAUTIFUL
GLAMOROUS MOVIE STAR —
OR EVEN A **WELL LIKED**
BEAUTIFUL GLAMOROUS
MOVIE STAR. I
JUST WANT
TO BE A
BEAUTIFUL
GLAMOROUS
MOVIE STAR
FOR ITS
OWN
SAKE.

Then as the moon lit the sky she returned home.

THIS IS
YOUR
FRIENDLY
NEIGHBORHOOD
GODMOTHER.
WHERE
YOU
BEEN?

YOUR FRIENDLY NEIGHBORHOOD
GODMOTHER ONLY HAS POWER
FROM "THE MICKEY MOUSE CLUB"
TO THE "LATE LATE SHOW."
DURING THOSE HOURS YOU
SHALL BE RAVISHING. YOU
SHALL BE **PASSIONELLA!**

A-AND THE
REST OF
THE DAY?

THE REST OF
THE DAY, MY
DEAR, YOU
ARE ON
SUSTAINING.

And with that her friendly neighborhood
godmother signed off.

in the months
that followed
a new star
was born:
the mysterious
exotic
bewitching
temptress...

Passionella

Prevue
PASSIONELLA
in
the SINNER

A legend grew around her. Strange stories circulated.
Stories of how she would only allow her films to be
shot between the hours of the 'Mickey Mouse Club'
and the 'Late Late Show' and how at 3 a.m. she
would hop into her sports car and vanish.

"WHO IS THIS MYSTERIOUS PASSIONELLA?" fans and
columnists wondered. "WHAT IS HER SECRET?"
asked show business.

And as her mystery grew, so did her popularity.
Her pictures set new attendance records.

Songs were written about her.

She was in demand everywhere.
And when there were no pictures
to make, life became a ceaseless
round of cocktail parties, night-
club parties, publicity parties,
beat parties.

But was Passionella happy? Now that she had money, fame, glamor, excitement - was she truly content?

Let us hear the answer in her own words:

"I AM NOT TRULY CONTENT."

She began to feel a vague discomfort -

A certain indefinable unhappiness.

"DON'T FEEL UNHAPPY" said her producers

and they bought her a new house.

"DON'T FEEL UNHAPPY" said her directors -

and they bought her a swimming pool for her new house.

"DON'T FEEL UNHAPPY" said her legion of faithful fans -

And they bought her a beach to go with the swimming pool of her new house.

But Passionella was still not happy...

WHAT DOES
IT ALL MEAN
IF I CAN
NOT HAVE
LOVE?

She spent her nights acting and her days weeping.

OH HOW
HOLLOW
IS ALL THIS
BEAUTY
WITHOUT
THE RIGHT
MAN TO
SHARE
IT
WITH.

Finally she spoke to her friendly neighborhood godmother

MY FIELD IS STRICTLY PUBLIC RELATIONS. YOU'LL HAVE TO HANDLE YOUR OWN EMOTIONAL PROBLEMS.

And then one day Passionella met the right man...

her
new
co-star-
the
idol
of
a
million
teenagers..
FLIP
(THE PRINCE)
CHARMING!

CRAZY

snap
snap
snap

The Prince represented the youth
movement in Hollywood.

He hated cops,

He hated reporters,

He hated movies.

COPS STINK

REPORTERS STINK

MOVIES STINK

snap

snap

snap

Passionella had never met such a man.

YOU DIG BECKETT, MAN?

WHO?

Glamor did not interest him.

YOU DIG BRECHT, MAN?

WHO? WHO?

Making love did not interest him.

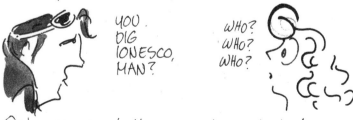

YOU DIG IONESCO, MAN?

WHO? WHO? WHO?

Only spiritual things interested him.

Passionella left him cold. He had but one passion.

ACTING, MAN, **ACTING!**
THE CHICK WHO MAKES
THIS CAT SWING HAS
GOT TO **E-MOTE**, MAN—
E-MOTE!

Act! In all her years as a movie star no one
had wanted Passionella to act.

"HOW DOES
ONE GO
ABOUT IT?"she asked
her beloved.

"MAN—"
he
replied,
"GO
TO
SCHOOL."

And she did.

Now, the 'Inner Me Acting Academy' was where all the movie stars went to learn how to act. It could take young, pretty, dimple cheeked starlets -

And after months of study teach them how to act like:

confused juvenile delinquents -   disillusioned drug addicts -   sensitive gun fighters -   misunderstood Nazis.

"SO THAT'S WHAT ACTING IS" mused Passionella

"YES" said the school master. "WE ARE LEARN-ING TO PORTRAY THE REAL PEOPLE."

The next day Passionella went to the head of her studio.

"I AM TIRED OF BEING A CARDBOARD FIGURE ON A TINSEL BACKGROUND." she said.

"OH" said the studio head.

So there it was. And there was nothing anybody could do about it. "IF I CAN NOT PLAY A CHIMNEY SWEEP I SHALL RETIRE FROM THE SCREEN."

So the studio gave in.

GLAMOR GIRL TO PORTRAY CHIMNEY SWEEP cried the newspapers.

Can she really act? asked the magazines.

And the world waited to find out.

amid the cinders a busty rose?

"The Chimney Sweep" was budgeted as a twenty million dollar production.

NEVER
BEFORE
SUCH
TURGID
REALISM!

drummed the
press agents

WE WILL
EVEN
SHOOT IT
IN THE
BRONX!

proclaimed the
publicists.

No expense was spared. The very best blacklisted screen writers were flown in from England to do the scenario.

Then came word that Passionella had consented to a **daytime** shooting schedule. A nation of 175 million reeled back, stunned. Passionella went on "Youth Wants To Know."

"YES, IRWIN. FROM NOW ON I WILL PERFORM **ONLY** DURING THE DAY."

In the weeks that followed the eyes of six continents fastened on a secluded mansion in Beverly Hills.

And then came the first day of shooting. Half a state gathered to see the **new** Passionella leave for the studio.

"MARVELOUS!" cried the
producer.
"UNBELIEVABLE!" cried the
director.
"I THINK SHE'S OVERACTING." muttered a
jealous star
from a rival studio.

WE WILL USE
NO DOUBLES!
announced the studio.

PASSIONELLA WILL
SWEEP ALL HER
OWN CHIMNEYS!

No one could remember a screen personality ever fitting a role so perfectly.

But every day promptly at six, as the sun began to go down, Passionella would hop into her sports car and vanish.

Finally the picture was completed. 'The Chimney Sweep' was previewed at a special showing for landlords.

It drew raves.

"AT LAST MOVIES HAVE COME OF AGE" said the Saturday Review.

"PASSIONELLA IS A CINCH TO COP THE OSCAR" said Hedda, Louella, Sidney, Sheila, Hy and Cholly Knickerbocker.

I COULD NEVER HAVE WON THIS WITHOUT THE ASSISTANCE OF THAT GREAT CREW OF GRIPS, GROPES, HEAVERS, GRAPPLERS AND BUILDING SUPERINTENDENTS WHO MADE THIS PICTURE POSSIBLE. said Passionella in her heart-warming acceptance speech.

The award was presented by last years winner,
FLIP (the Prince) CHARMING — who whispered:

Their engage-
ment was
announced
on the spot.

Dreamy eyed, the two lovers went home where
they passed the night making tender love.

And then..

It was three a.m. The two lovers stared
at each other aghast.

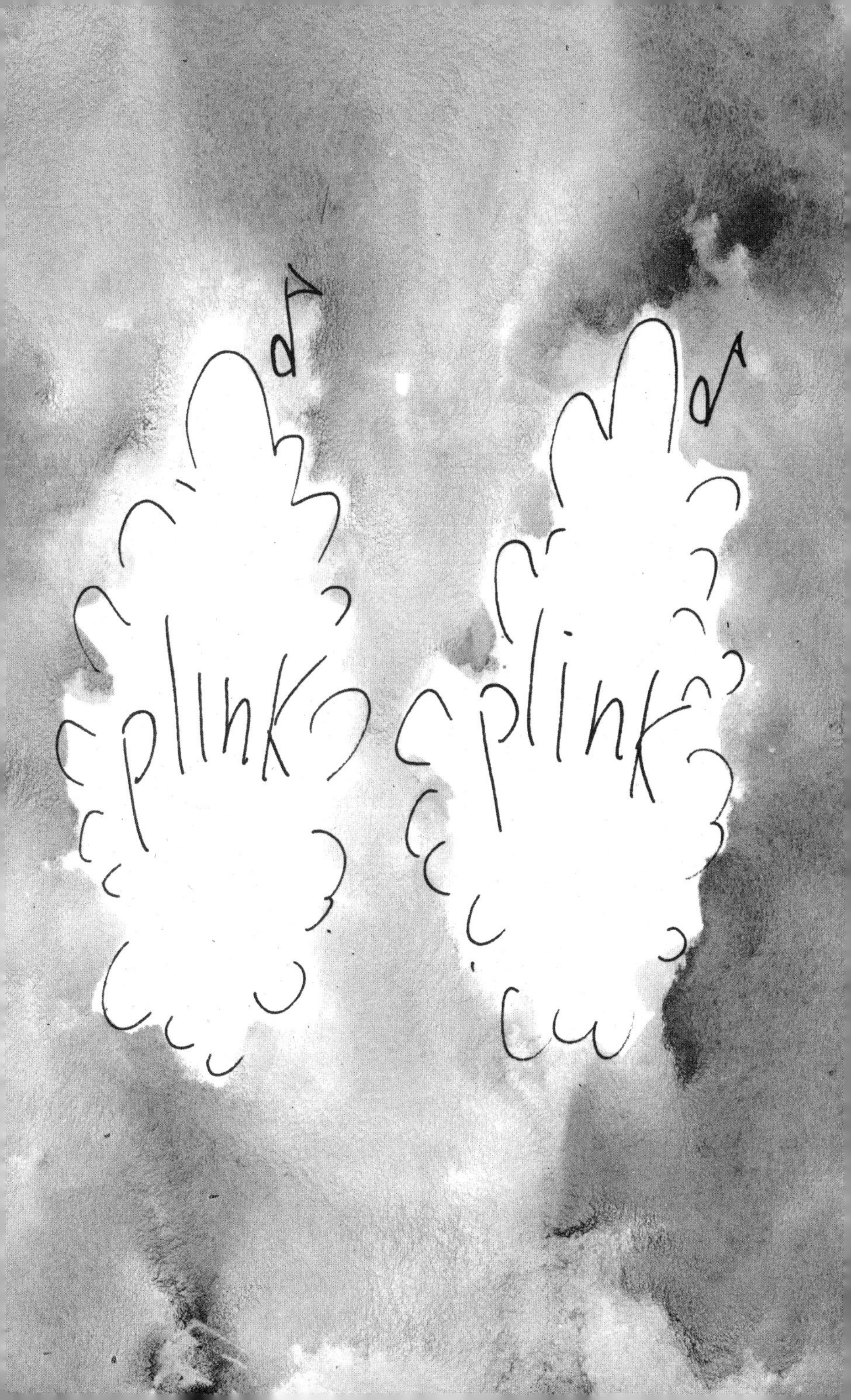
plink
plink

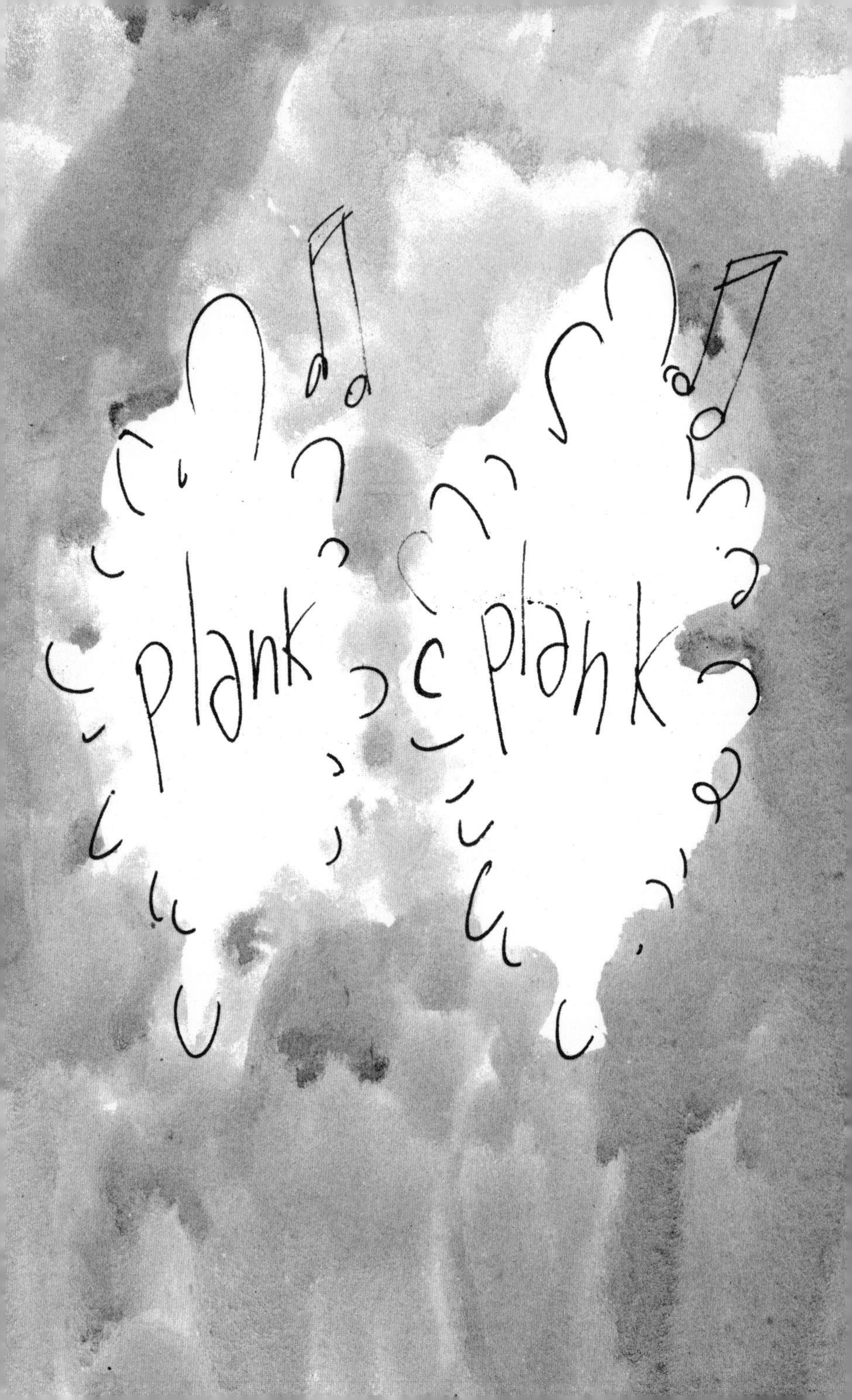
plank
plank

And they lived happily ever after.

Munro

Now
this
is
all
about
Munro

who was four

There was nothing unusual about Munro.

He wouldn't eat. NO!

He wouldn't sleep. NO!

He hated little girls. GRRR!

His was a stable, well rounded, fully integrated life.
Then one day he received a letter...

He had one of his big friends read it to him.

IT'S FROM LOCAL
DRAFT BOARD 92
AND IT SAYS
YOUR FRIENDS
AND NEIGHBORS
SEND YOU
GREETINGS.

So while other children jumped rope and hula hooped and chased each other around the block, and did exactly what it was normal for them to do, Munro came to the shocking realization that at the age of four, **he** had been drafted.

The next morning without telling his mother (she always took on so) Munro went for his physical.

UNBUTTON ME, MISTER.

He took a whole series of tests. He took an intelligence test,...

and a height test.

HEIGHT: SIX FOOT TWO!

All along Munro tried to explain that he was just a little boy - but the doctors were too busy drafting famous singer to ever even notice him.

And so Munro was classified 1A.

BUTTON
ME,
MISTER.

Of course, Munro didn't say anything for fear someone might call him unpatriotic. He went on home and didn't tell a soul. (His mother always took on so.)

In twenty one days a second letter came. This one was from the **President** himself, which made Munro feel better about the whole thing.

So with a bar of soap, some chocolate cigarettes and a toothbrush, Munro went to war.

Char

The Sergeant couldn't speak English very well.

FOOR'RIT HOO

He spoke in code.

HUP
HOOP
HIP
HO
HUP
HOO
HIP
HO

Munro thought he was crazy.

First thing, Munro and all the others were marched off to a big hall to hear an important looking man talk. The man explained they were all there because of a world struggle. It seemed that one side was in favor of God and the other was not. The man used very simple words. Even Munro could understand.

When the man was finished, everyone was marched off again.

Now Munro was a full fledged soldier.

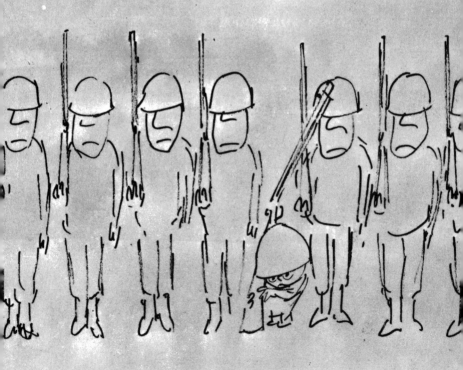

He learned to play
all the games
that soldiers play..
like "FACE"...

RI' FACE
LEF' FACE
UP FACE
DOWN FACE
IN FACE
OUT FACE
FACE FACE

Or another game called "TAKE THIS MAN'S NAME" where
everyone must sweep and clean to make the barracks
as shiny as they could ever be and then the man who
was "IT" would walk past each bunk with a cranky
look on his face and say:

TAKE THIS MAN'S NAME!
TAKE THIS MAN'S NAME!
TAKE ...

Or another game called "BENDOVER" where if you are "IT", you had to go to the kitchen and bendover while you

mopped floors

cleaned stoves

washed out garbage cans

Oh, there were so many games to play. Just when Munro would think they were all out along came a new one.

After awhile he grew tired of playing.
He lost all his zest for

mud

guns

food

But the sergeants

And the captains

And the colonels

And the generals -

always loved to play   They never seemed
to get tired.

But poor Munro was very tired. So he went to the sergeant and he said:

The sergeant did not look up. Sergeants are very busy people.

The sergeant still did not look up. The way to always tell its a sergeant is if he doesn't ever look up. Finally he said.

IT IS THE OFFICIAL POLICY OF THE ARMY NOT TO DRAFT MEN OF FOUR. ERGO YOU CANNOT BE FOUR. ERGO YOU ONLY **THINK** YOU ARE FOUR. GO ON SICK CALL.

So the next morning Munro went on sick call.

Sick call was held in a big crowded room. Some times it was drafty. Sometimes it was over heated. "KEEPS THEM ON THEIR TOES" reasoned the policy makers. Every once in a while a doctor would walk through the room, muttering in a low voice...

Finally it was Munro's turn.

Munro was sent on his way with a box of white pills and a warning to stop faking. Sick call was over.

But try as he might, Munro just could not get over the idea that he was four. He went to the psychiatrist.

.. analyzed the psychiatrist.

He went to the chaplain.

MY SON, YOU WILL FIND
LIFE HERE IN THE ARMY
SO MUCH MORE REWARD-
ING IF YOU MAKE THE
BEST OF IT AND DECIDE
TO FACE REALITIES. LETS
HAVE ANOTHER CHAT
REAL SOON.

...quoth the chaplain.

He went to a colonel.

GET OUTTA HERE Y'LITTLE GOOFUP OR I'LL SHOVE YA IN THE STOCKADE FOR A MONTH!

... opined the colonel.

He went before a whole board of captains and majors and colonels who had all once been social workers on the lower east side so that they **understood** about people. They stared at Munro a long time. Then they said:

GO BACK AND TRY!

Munro promised he would try - really try this time. For if so many wise men claimed it was impossible for him to be four, how indeed could he be?

So Munro returned to the barracks, his little back aching, his little legs weary. This was to be his life from now on.

He would march with the best of them.

He would shoot with the best of them.

And, if need be, he would go to war with the best of them.

And as he walked he saw a **new** bunch of men - all marching along out of step - all looking very unhappy.

Munro just stood there and watched.

"SEE THAT MAN!" said the sergeant suddenly pointing at Munro. All the new men looked.

"THAT'S A **SOLDIER!**" said the sergeant proudly. "THAT'S WHAT WE'RE GOING TO TRAIN **YOU** TO BE!"

All the men looked

"WE'RE GOING TO SEPARATE THE MEN FROM THE BOYS!" said the sergeant.

And Munro began to cry.

Right there in the middle of the field, he cried and cried.

"STOP THAT CRYING, SOLDIER!" said the sergeant and he looked embarrassed.

Munro cried louder.

"STOP THAT CRYING, SOLDIER!" said the colonel and he came running out of his office looking very upset.

Monro only cried louder.

Out ran the doctor.

Out ran the psychiatrist.

Out ran the chaplain.

No one had heard such a sound in the middle of an army camp before.

"STOP! YOU **MUST** STOP THAT CRYING, SOLDIER!" they all said.

But Munro wouldn't.

Then out came the general.

Everyone stepped back. Everyone saluted.

Except Munro - who cried.

"SOLDIERS DON'T CRY" said the general.
Everyone nodded.

Munro cried.

"ONLY LITTLE BOYS CRY." said the general. Everyone nodded.

Munro cried.

"ARE YOU A SOLDIER OR A LITTLE TEENSY WEENSY HELPLESS CRYING BABY BOY?" demanded the general.

"YEAH!" said everybody.

Munro just cried.

The general stared at him scornfully.
"OBVIOUSLY THEN YOU'RE NOTHING BUT A **LITTLE BABY BOY!**"

"*OBVIOUSLY*" said the colonel scornfully.

"OBVIOUSLY," said the doctor, the chaplain, the psychiatrist, the whole board of captains and majors and colonels scornfully.

"OBVIOUSLY" said the new bunch of men.

And suddenly- once they had said it-
Munro looked different to them.

He looked like **a little boy!**

The general blinked his eyes
and stared very hard.

He stared harder than he'd ever
stared in his whole life.

And then finally he said:

I RULE THAT **THIS** IS A LITTLE BOY.

Everyone nodded in agreement. "WHO COULD EVER THINK THIS WAS ANYTHING BUT A LITTLE BOY." they said. And they made out it was all a big joke.

They pinched Munro's cheeks.

They tousled his hair.

They gave him a release to sign.

The day Munro was sent home they held
a big parade in his honor.

There were newsreel photographers and live television and his mother and his father and all the kids in the neighborhood and even another message from the President—

"I HOLD NO FEAR FOR OUR NATION'S FUTURE WHEN EVEN A MERE LAD OF FOUR IS STIRRED STRONGLY ENOUGH BY OUR CAUSE TO ENLIST HIMSELF IN THE SERVICE OF HIS COUNTRY."

And a man from the American Legion came around asking him to join.

He was awarded a medal, a set of military brushes, and a whole box of toy nuclear weapons.
Munro was a hero!

Oh, his parents were **very** proud.

But, from that time on, whenever he became cranky—

and wouldn't eat—

No!

and wouldn't sleep—

No!

and hated little girls—

GRRR!

his mother would just remind him of the army—

and Munro would be a good boy -

a very good boy indeed.

George's
Moon

Once

here was a man named George —

who lived on the moon —

no kidding.

George didn't have much to do on the moon.

He slept.

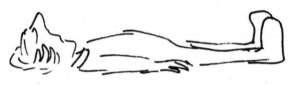

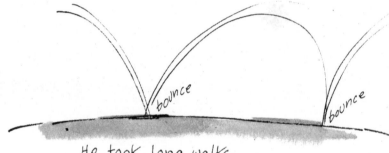

He took long walks.

He kept trying to figure
out how he got there.

THERE **MUST**
BE A
LOGICAL
EXPLANATION.

But he never made any headway.

Aside from feeling that he was basically **non-moon**, he had no idea **who** he was or **how** he got there. All he knew definitely was that undoubtedly his name **was** George.

ONE **MUST** BEGIN SOMEWHERE.

And that somehow he was unique.

3.

HI THERE,
MY MOON.

4.

5.

SOMEDAY
I'LL CHANGE
YOUR NAME
TO **GEORGE**.

6.

But this was a false exuberance. George felt no real connection with the land.

HOW CAN I WHEN I BOUNCE ALL THE TIME.

Mostly he was concerned with his **roots**. He thought about his roots quite a bit. But no matter how hard he thought he couldn't come up with a thing.

— SIGH.

So then he'd concentrate on his values. Because if he could sort out his values it would tell him something about his background and if he knew something about his background it would then give him some indication of his roots.

5/64.

But he couldn't come up with a single value.

All of which was pretty depressing.

One day George decided:

MY TROUBLE IS I'M TOO INTROSPECTIVE.

I NEED SOME OUTSIDE INTERESTS.

So he began a rock collection.

Rocks had no meaning for George. He began to count craters.

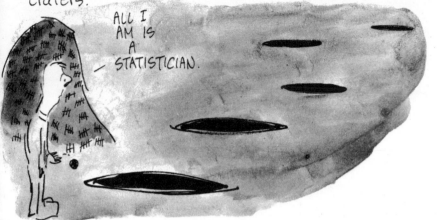

George felt he was thinking too much. He needed to regain the feeling of his body. So he learned to drop kick his rock collection into his craters.

But he ran out of rocks.

He was just filling up time and he knew it. What good was it to collect rocks, to count craters, to fill the craters you've counted with the rocks you've collected, to empty the craters and collect the rocks all over again?
Was this a way for a man to spend a life?

IT LACKS DIGNITY.

George recognized he had no sense of himself. Also that he had no sense of others. How could he have any dignity without a context? He didn't know who he was or what or anything.

A MAN **HAS** TO BELIEVE IN SOMETHING.

So since **he** was the only thing around, George decided to believe in himself.

HAIL GEORGE.

He made up poems to himself.

GEORGE
George
GEORGE
george
GEORGE
George
GEORGE,

He made up stories to himself.

SO GEORGE CURED THE PLAGUE, ENDED THE FAMINE, TURNED BACK THE FLOOD.

And then he awoke one morning and found that he had forgotten his name.

THAT'S WHAT I GET. SERVES ME RIGHT.

So he stopped believing in himself.

He looked around for something
else to believe in. He tried to
believe in rocks.

HAIL.

But they seemed so ordinary.

He tried to believe in craters.

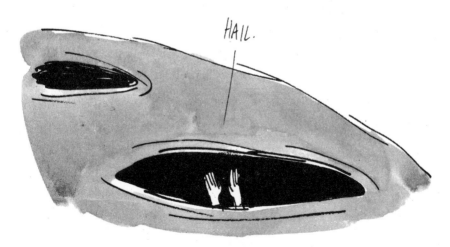

HAIL.

But since he had kicked rocks into them
he hadn't much respect for craters.

He made up other things to believe in. But they were all inadequate. He needed something spectacular. Something way beyond his experience. Then one day he looked up and noticed space.

There were all sorts of advantages to believing in space.
For one thing it was out there - **way** out there —

AND IT
FILLS UP
EVERYTHING.
THAT'S PRETTY
IMPRESSIVE.

And it was obviously unknown.

IT COULD
NEVER BE
DISILLUSIONING.

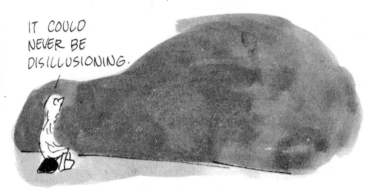

And it was dark with white blotches - very attractive
really - much more imposing than all those rocks
and craters he **used** to worship.

IT'S AMAZING
HOW I'VE
MATURED IN
MY BELIEFS.

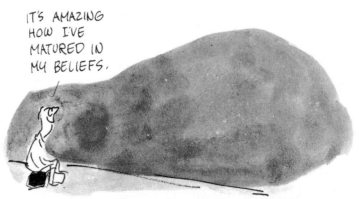

George spent his days dreaming about space.

IF SPACE IS **REALLY** THERE AND I **KNOW** IT MUST BE THERE BECAUSE I CAN SEE IT.

THEN **I** MUST BE REALLY **HERE** OR ELSE I WOULDN'T KNOW ITS **THERE** BECAUSE I COULDN'T SEE IT.

AND IF I **AM** HERE AND **I** CAN SEE SPACE THEN SPACE MUST, IN ALL LOGIC, BE ABLE TO SEE **ME**.

—WHICH PROVES THAT I **EXIST**.

SPACE AND GEORGE— GEORGE AND SPACE—

A TEAM.

It almost made him feel like crying.

hen one day they started shooting rockets off
at him.

George was overjoyed.

George tied a red undershirt to a big rock.

But the rocket didn't even come close.

George wasn't too sad, Space was no longer mysterious and intangible. Space had people in it and they were trying to rescue him. He sat all day on the dark side and dreamed about them:

FIRST OF ALL THEY MUST BE VERY KIND TO GO TO ALL THIS TROUBLE. THEY MUST BE VERY HUMAN-ITARIAN AND HAVE LOTS OF FAVORITE CHARITIES.

THEY WILL COME HERE AND WE'LL HAVE A BIG PARTY AND I'LL BE VERY POLITE AND ASK THEM IF THEY'D LIKE TO STAY OVER BUT THEY'LL SAY - "WELL, WE **DO** HAVE TO GET BACK."

AND THEN WE'LL TAKE OFF AND I'LL BE **HOME** (WHEREVER THAT IS) AND THERE'LL BE BIG PARADES AND TESTIMONIAL DINNERS.

ALL BECAUSE **I'M** THE ONLY EXPERT ON THE MOON!

But then George realized he **wasn't** an expert on the moon. In fact he really didn't know much about it at all.

He didn't know whether those holes actually **were** craters or not. Maybe they were coal mines.

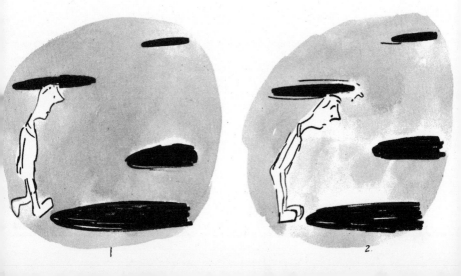

He didn't know why it was that he could bounce or how come he could breathe without a helmet or why he was never hungry though there wasn't any food to eat.

MY TROUBLE IS I'M NOT VERY OBSERV- ANT.

THEY'LL COME EXPECTING ALL KINDS OF INFORMA- TION AND WHAT CAN I TELL THEM?

NOTHING!

OH, I'M SURE THEY'LL BE VERY NICE ABOUT IT. THEY'LL PRETEND NOT EVEN TO NOTICE.

THEY'LL SAY- "MY, BUT DON'T YOU DRESS NEATLY."

I'LL FEEL LIKE A FOOL!

And then one day they shot off another rocket.

George hung up his undershirt again but on a less conspicuous rock. He began to feel anxious about the whole thing.

WHAT DO THEY WANT FROM ME? I'M NOT ANALYTICAL. THEY'LL JUST HAVE TO UNDERSTAND.

A FAT LOT **THEY'LL** CARE! THEY'LL BE **SCIENTISTS!** COLD- DISPASSIONATE— NO TIME FOR **MY** PROBLEMS.

THEY PROBABLY
DON'T EVEN
KNOW I'M
HERE!

But once more the rocket did not come close.

WISE
GUYS.

But George knew that ultimately they **would** come.
He spent all his days sitting on the dark side
and dreaming about what it would be like.

THEY'LL COME OUT OF
THOSE DAMN ROCKETS
AND I BET FIRST
THING THEY'LL DO IS
STICK UP A **FLAG**

THEIR
FLAG
ON MY
MOON!

THEN THEY'LL
GIVE ME THEIR
BAGS TO CARRY.

THEY'LL MAKE FUN OF ME -
"YOU MEAN **YOU** DIDN'T
KNOW ABOUT **GRAVITY**?
YOU HEAR THAT GANG?
BEEN ON THE MOON
ALL THIS
TIME AND
HE DIDN'T
KNOW
ABOUT
GRAVITY!"

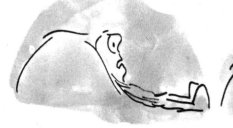

AND THEY'LL
TELL LOTS
OF INSIDE
JOKES.

"WELL WE'D **LOVE** TO TAKE
YOU BACK" THEY'LL SAY-
"BUT YOU SEE HOW
CROWDED WE ARE WITH
ALL THESE ROCK
SAMPLES. WOULD YOU
MIND GIVING US A
SHOVE?"

George thought about the way it used to be. The fun he had drop kicking rocks into craters. What a ball it was to sit around the moon and think about his roots.

THEY'VE
SPOILED
IT!

And then one day they shot off another rocket.

George used body english to make it go away.

But the rocket kept coming—

ITS AN INVASION!

Then, suddenly the fear and indecision which had held him for weeks was no more. George knew what he had to do.

THIS
IS
WAR!

I DON'T CARE HOW MANY ROCKS THEY HAVE. I KNOW THE TERRAIN.

and he patiently waited.

Boom !

Once...

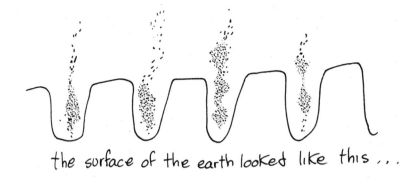

the surface of the earth looked like this ...

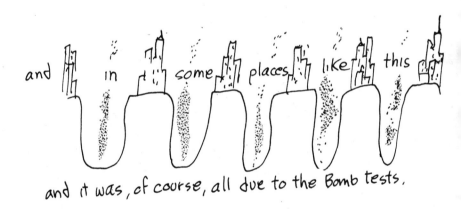

and in some places like this

and it was, of course, all due to the Bomb tests.

Almost every country had its own Bomb.

If you've got a Bomb you're supposed to test it.

Like to see if it works.

After each explosion the test areas were filled by government scientists who took readings and checked their instruments and issued a definitive statement.

"THIS TEST HAS ADDED NO APPRECIABLE AMOUNT OF RADIO ACTIVE FALLOUT TO THE ATMOSPHERE"

Naturally the more tests there were the better the Bombs got to be.

But the skies began to grow darker

and people noticed it and said:

"I GUESS THE GOVERNMENT MUST HAVE ITS SOUND REASONS"

and went about their business.

of course there was more going on than just Bomb tests.
For instance, as soon as one country discovered a bigger Bomb than its neighbor

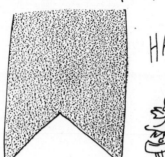

HA!

sigh

the first thing it did was call a disarmament conference-

and make a proposal-

"LETS ALL STOP WHERE WE ARE RIGHT NOW. ALL THOSE IN FAVOR OF PEACE SAY 'AYE!'"

and all the other countries replied:
"WE AGREE. JUST AS SOON AS WE CATCH UP."

So there was a deadlock

and people heard the news and said:
"THATS THE WAY THE BALL BOUNCES" or "THATS THE WAY THE COOKIE CRUMBLES."

and went about their business.

But the conferences continued,

while more and more countries developed their own Bomb. And naturally all of them had to be invited,

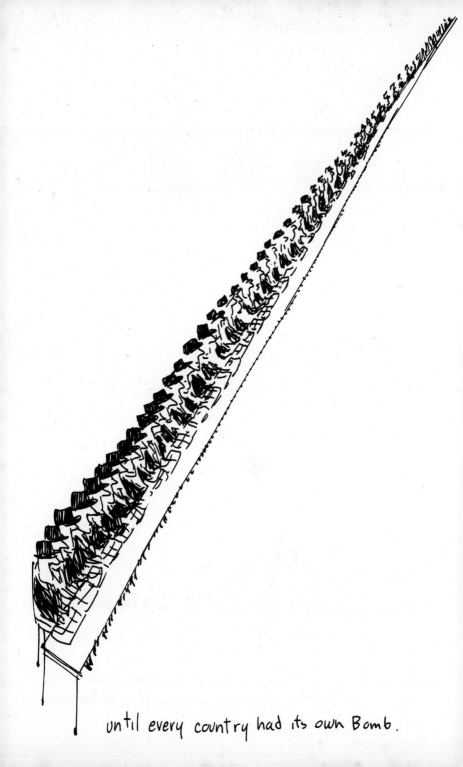

until every country had its own Bomb.

and even some towns..

and even:

and people heard the news and said:

"THATS THE WAY THE ONION PEELS"

and went about their business.

Each test, no matter how small, was carefully checked for after effects. "THIS TEST HAS ADDED NO APPRECIABLE AMOUNT OF RADIO ACTIVE FALL OUT TO THE ATMOSPHERE."

But now the skies began to look like this.

and people noticed it and said:

"OF COURSE I'M CONCERNED BUT
WHAT CAN ONE PERSON DO?"

and went about their business.

The government began to get worried.

"PEOPLE MAY GET
TO THINK THOSE
BIG BLACK FLOATING
SPECKS ARE
HARMFUL."

"WE MUST
REASSURE
THEM."

So they hired a public relations outfit...

BIG BLACK FLOATING
SPECKS ARE
VERY PRETTY!

BIG BLACK FLOATING
SPECKS ARE
GOOD FOR YOU!

which put on a big campaign.

But the campaign had no effect. People got more and more concerned.

Then the public relations outfit changed its tactics.

The public responded sympathetically. "WE'RE ON THE RIGHT TRACK AT LAST" said the public relations outfit.

BIG BLACK FLOAT-ING SPECK FILTERS

BIG BLACK FLOATING SPECK PROOF EYE GLASSES

BIG BLACK FLOATING SPECK PROOF TRANQUILIZERS

Industry thrived.

World economy boomed.

The problem of over-population seemed somehow to diminish.

BASH

With the thickening of the specks, new businesses were born. The world grew rich. Education prospered. Art flourished.

It was a new renaissance

But soon countries grew fat and complacent. Bomb production dropped off. And then – one day – the black specks began to disappear.

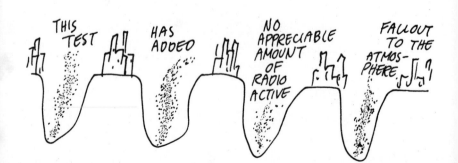

So while half the people in the world worked
on new improved Bombs—

SECRET

the other half worked on salves, medication,
and storm windows.

And people saw the situation and said:

"THATS THE WAY THE SPEARMINT CHEWS"—

and went about their business.

Then one day...

"GENTLEMEN, I MAY BE TALKING OFF THE TOP OF MY HEAD — BUT I THINK I'VE DREAMED UP A BOMB THAT WILL BLOW UP THE WHOLE WORKS!"

"WHAT A DETERRENT FOR PEACE" said men on the inside.

But prop-agandists in other countries planted seeds of doubt.

NON-SENSE!

BALONEY

BLUFF!

So the men on the inside got together —

"THIS DETERRENT WILL NEVER BE EFFECTIVE UNTIL WE TEST IT!"

But nobody wanted to take the blame. "HEY!" said somebody, "WHY DON'T WE TAKE THE QUESTION TO THE PEOPLE!"

So it was decided. A referendum was announced.

Men on the inside campaigned vigorously.

THIS TEST WILL ADD NO APPRECIABLE AMOUNT OF RADIOACTIVE FALLOUT TO THE ATMOSPHERE.

The test was given an overwhelming mandate. the people said:

"NOW IS NO TIME TO SHOW LACK OF UNITY"

and they went about their business.

So they had the test.

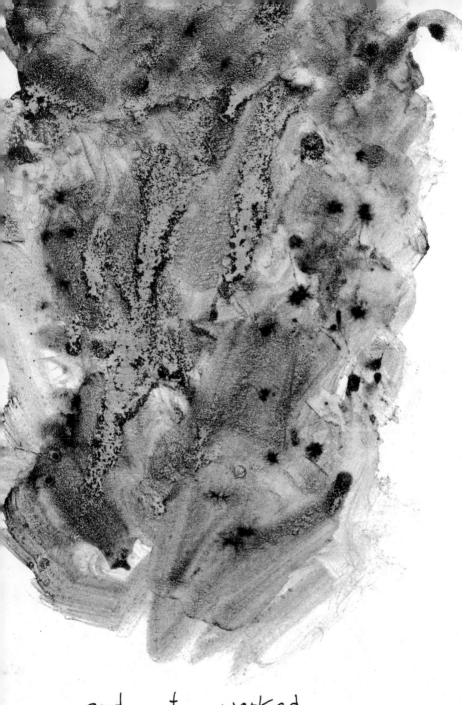

and it worked.